AF753080

GENERAL LEDGER

GENERAL LEDGER

ACCOUNT *Cash* ACCOUNT NO. *1110*

DATE		ITEM	POST. REF.	DEBIT	CREDIT	BALANCE	
						DEBIT	CREDIT
20--							
Apr.	1	Balance	✓			84,147.80	

ACCOUNT *Notes Receivable* ACCOUNT NO. *1111*

DATE		ITEM	POST. REF.	DEBIT	CREDIT	BALANCE	
						DEBIT	CREDIT
20--							
Apr.	1	Balance	✓			9,800.00	

ACCOUNT *Accounts Receivable* ACCOUNT NO. *1112*

DATE		ITEM	POST. REF.	DEBIT	CREDIT	BALANCE	
						DEBIT	CREDIT
20--							
Apr.	1	Balance	✓			52,136.00	

ACCOUNT *Interest Receivable* ACCOUNT NO. *1113*

DATE		ITEM	POST. REF.	DEBIT	CREDIT	BALANCE	
						DEBIT	CREDIT

ACCOUNT *Merchandise Inventory* ACCOUNT NO. *1114*

DATE		ITEM	POST. REF.	DEBIT	CREDIT	BALANCE DEBIT	BALANCE CREDIT
20--							
Apr.	1	Balance	✓			240 9 0 0 00	

ACCOUNT *Estimated Returns Inventory* ACCOUNT NO. *1115*

DATE		ITEM	POST. REF.	DEBIT	CREDIT	BALANCE DEBIT	BALANCE CREDIT
20--							
Apr.	1	Balance	✓			2 3 5 7 00	

ACCOUNT *Office Supplies* ACCOUNT NO. *1116*

DATE		ITEM	POST. REF.	DEBIT	CREDIT	BALANCE DEBIT	BALANCE CREDIT
20--							
Apr.	1	Balance	✓			2 1 0 0 00	

ACCOUNT *Store Supplies* ACCOUNT NO. *1117*

DATE		ITEM	POST. REF.	DEBIT	CREDIT	BALANCE DEBIT	BALANCE CREDIT
20--							
Apr.	1	Balance	✓			1 6 8 0 00	

ACCOUNT *Prepaid Insurance* ACCOUNT NO. *1118*

DATE		ITEM	POST. REF.	DEBIT	CREDIT	BALANCE DEBIT	BALANCE CREDIT

ACCOUNT *Land* ACCOUNT NO. *1120*

DATE		ITEM	POST. REF.	DEBIT	CREDIT	BALANCE DEBIT	BALANCE CREDIT
20--							
Apr.	1	Balance	✓			210 0 0 0 00	

ACCOUNT *Building* ACCOUNT NO. *1122*

DATE		ITEM	POST. REF.	DEBIT	CREDIT	BALANCE DEBIT	BALANCE CREDIT
20--							
Apr.	1	Balance	✓			439 0 0 0 00	

ACCOUNT *Accumulated Depreciation—Building* ACCOUNT NO. *1123*

DATE		ITEM	POST. REF.	DEBIT	CREDIT	BALANCE DEBIT	BALANCE CREDIT
20--							
Apr.	1	Balance	✓				140,200.00

ACCOUNT *Equipment* ACCOUNT NO. *1124*

DATE		ITEM	POST. REF.	DEBIT	CREDIT	BALANCE DEBIT	BALANCE CREDIT
20--							
Apr.	1	Balance	✓			98,350.00	

ACCOUNT *Accumulated Depreciation—Equipment* ACCOUNT NO. *1125*

DATE		ITEM	POST. REF.	DEBIT	CREDIT	BALANCE DEBIT	BALANCE CREDIT
20--							
Apr.	1	Balance	✓				34,540.00

ACCOUNT *Accounts Payable* ACCOUNT NO. *2100*

DATE		ITEM	POST. REF.	DEBIT	CREDIT	BALANCE DEBIT	BALANCE CREDIT
20--							
Apr.	1	Balance	✓				127,948.80

ACCOUNT *Salaries Payable* ACCOUNT NO. *2110*

DATE		ITEM	POST. REF.	DEBIT	CREDIT	BALANCE DEBIT	BALANCE CREDIT

ACCOUNT *Customer Refunds Payable* ACCOUNT NO. *2120*

DATE		ITEM	POST. REF.	DEBIT	CREDIT	BALANCE DEBIT	BALANCE CREDIT
20--							
Apr.	*1*	*Balance*					*3300 00*

ACCOUNT *Notes Payable* ACCOUNT NO. *2150*

DATE		ITEM	POST. REF.	DEBIT	CREDIT	BALANCE DEBIT	BALANCE CREDIT
20--							
Apr.	*1*	*Balance*	✓				*168000 00*

ACCOUNT *Marty Chavez, Capital* ACCOUNT NO. *3100*

DATE		ITEM	POST. REF.	DEBIT	CREDIT	BALANCE DEBIT	BALANCE CREDIT
20--							
Apr.	*1*	*Balance*	✓				*666,482.00*

ACCOUNT *Marty Chavez, Drawing* ACCOUNT NO. *3110*

DATE		ITEM	POST. REF.	DEBIT	CREDIT	BALANCE DEBIT	BALANCE CREDIT

ACCOUNT *Income Summary* ACCOUNT NO. *3120*

DATE		ITEM	POST. REF.	DEBIT	CREDIT	BALANCE DEBIT	BALANCE CREDIT

ACCOUNT *Sales* ACCOUNT NO. *4100*

DATE	ITEM	POST. REF.	DEBIT	CREDIT	BALANCE	
					DEBIT	CREDIT

ACCOUNT *Cost of Merchandise Sold* ACCOUNT NO. *5100*

DATE	ITEM	POST. REF.	DEBIT	CREDIT	BALANCE	
					DEBIT	CREDIT

ACCOUNT *Sales Salaries Expense* ACCOUNT NO. *5200*

DATE	ITEM	POST. REF.	DEBIT	CREDIT	BALANCE	
					DEBIT	CREDIT

ACCOUNT *Advertising Expense* ACCOUNT NO. *5210*

DATE	ITEM	POST. REF.	DEBIT	CREDIT	BALANCE	
					DEBIT	CREDIT

ACCOUNT *Store Supplies Expense* ACCOUNT NO. *5220*

DATE	ITEM	POST. REF.	DEBIT	CREDIT	BALANCE	
					DEBIT	CREDIT

ACCOUNT *Miscellaneous Selling Expense* ACCOUNT NO. *5290*

DATE	ITEM	POST. REF.	DEBIT	CREDIT	BALANCE	
					DEBIT	CREDIT

ACCOUNT *Office Salaries Expense* ACCOUNT NO. *5300*

DATE		ITEM	POST. REF.	DEBIT	CREDIT	BALANCE	
						DEBIT	CREDIT

ACCOUNT *Depreciation Expense—Equipment* ACCOUNT NO. *5320*

DATE		ITEM	POST. REF.	DEBIT	CREDIT	BALANCE	
						DEBIT	CREDIT

ACCOUNT *Insurance Expense* ACCOUNT NO. *5330*

DATE		ITEM	POST. REF.	DEBIT	CREDIT	BALANCE	
						DEBIT	CREDIT

ACCOUNT *Office Supplies Expense* ACCOUNT NO. *5340*

DATE		ITEM	POST. REF.	DEBIT	CREDIT	BALANCE	
						DEBIT	CREDIT

ACCOUNT *Depreciation Expense—Building* ACCOUNT NO. *5350*

DATE		ITEM	POST. REF.	DEBIT	CREDIT	BALANCE	
						DEBIT	CREDIT

ACCOUNT *Miscellaneous Administrative Expense* ACCOUNT NO. *5390*

DATE		ITEM	POST. REF.	DEBIT	CREDIT	BALANCE	
						DEBIT	CREDIT

ACCOUNT *Interest Revenue* ACCOUNT NO. *6100*

DATE		ITEM	POST. REF.	DEBIT	CREDIT	BALANCE	
						DEBIT	CREDIT

ACCOUNT *Interest Expense* ACCOUNT NO. *7100*

DATE		ITEM	POST. REF.	DEBIT	CREDIT	BALANCE	
						DEBIT	CREDIT

ACCOUNTS RECEIVABLE LEDGER

ACCOUNTS RECEIVABLE LEDGER

NAME *All Access Fitness Centers*

ADDRESS *1 South Park Blvd., South Miami, FL 33143*

DATE		ITEM	POST. REF.	DEBIT	CREDIT	BALANCE

NAME *Body Excellence Fitness Club*

ADDRESS *9 Key Biscayne Ave., Suite 100, Key Biscayne, FL 33149*

DATE		ITEM	POST. REF.	DEBIT	CREDIT	BALANCE
20--						
Apr.	*1*	*Balance*	✓			*14,406.00*

NAME *Cory's Gym in the Grove*

ADDRESS *20 Main Highway, Coconut Grove, FL 33133*

DATE		ITEM	POST. REF.	DEBIT	CREDIT	BALANCE
20--						
Apr.	*1*	*Balance*	✓			*12,348.00*

NAME *Miami Health Club*

ADDRESS *8050 SW 8th Street, Miami, FL 33130*

DATE		ITEM	POST. REF.	DEBIT	CREDIT	BALANCE

NAME *Pine Bay Fitness Club*

ADDRESS *8 SW 57th Ave., Miami, FL 33156*

DATE		ITEM	POST. REF.	DEBIT	CREDIT	BALANCE
20--						
Apr.	*1*	*Balance*	✓			*10976 00*

NAME *Rockdale Gym*

ADDRESS *162 S. Dixie Hwy, Rockdale, FL 33157*

DATE		ITEM	POST. REF.	DEBIT	CREDIT	BALANCE

NAME *The Sun Set Recreation Centers*

ADDRESS *50 Snapper Creek Dr., Sunset, FL 33173*

DATE		ITEM	POST. REF.	DEBIT	CREDIT	BALANCE
20--						
Apr.	1	Balance	✓			6,174 00

NAME *Westwood Boxing Gym*

ADDRESS *50 Westwood Lake Dr., Miami, FL 33165*

DATE		ITEM	POST. REF.	DEBIT	CREDIT	BALANCE
20--						
Apr.	1	Balance	✓			8,232 00

NAME

ADDRESS

DATE		ITEM	POST. REF.	DEBIT	CREDIT	BALANCE

ACCOUNTS PAYABLE LEDGER

ACCOUNTS PAYABLE LEDGER

NAME *Alexus Fitness Connection*

ADDRESS *100 Coral Way, Miami, FL 33129*

DATE		ITEM	POST. REF.	DEBIT	CREDIT	BALANCE
20--						
Apr.	1	Balance	✓			142,688.80

NAME *Fit & Fab Health Products*

ADDRESS *15 Park Avenue, 115th Floor, New York, NY 10154*

DATE		ITEM	POST. REF.	DEBIT	CREDIT	BALANCE

NAME *Fizzy-Cal Network*

ADDRESS *45 Caribbean Avenue, Los Angeles, CA 90001*

DATE		ITEM	POST. REF.	DEBIT	CREDIT	BALANCE
20--						
Apr.	1	Balance	✓			464,800.00

NAME *HeartFit Enterprises*

ADDRESS *15 Brickell Ave. #150, Miami, FL 33129*

DATE		ITEM	POST. REF.	DEBIT	CREDIT	BALANCE
20--						
Apr.	1	Balance	✓			14 000 00

NAME *Muscles R_X Distributors*

ADDRESS *80 Commercial Blvd., Fort Lauderdale, FL 33310*

DATE		ITEM	POST. REF.	DEBIT	CREDIT	BALANCE
20--						
Apr.	1	Balance	✓			53 200 00

NAME *Sports Magic Warehouse*

ADDRESS *246 Santa Monica Blvd., Santa Monica, CA 90403*

DATE		ITEM	POST. REF.	DEBIT	CREDIT	BALANCE